Take-Along
LARGE PRINT WORD-FINDS ™

Volume 10

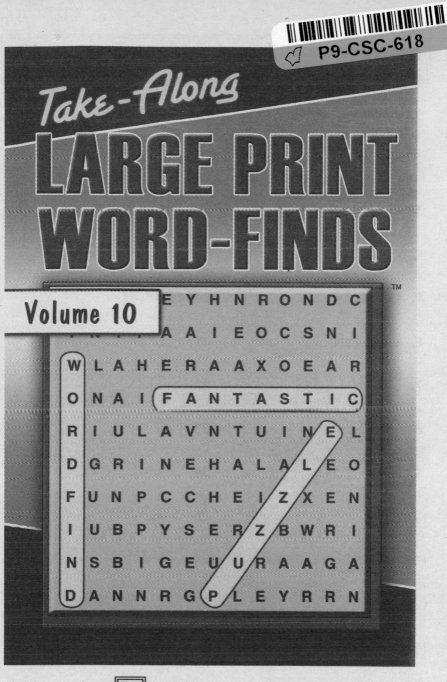

K **KAPPA Books**
A Division of KAPPA Graphics, L.P.

1 THE TETONS

1. BERRIES
2. BRIDGER
3. CAMP
4. CASCADE
5. CHAPEL
6. COLTER BAY
7. ELEVATION
8. GEYSER
9. GRAND
10. HIKE
11. JACKSON HOLE
12. JAGGED
13. MOOSE
14. MOUNTAIN
15. NATIONAL PARK
16. OLD WEST
17. PASS
18. PEAKS
19. RENDEZVOUS
20. RESORT
21. ROCKIES
22. SIOUX
23. SKI
24. SNAKE RIVER
25. SNOW
26. TRADE
27. WYOMING
28. YELLOWSTONE

```
R T R O S E R J N G R A N D
R E V I R E K A N S W E O I
N S G L H S I C J C S K I Q
T A S D K T A K A Q E I T Y
O S T A I M P S C W I H A S
U W E I P R C O M O R B V U
V P S W O A B N C E R S E O
W A S N D N H H S E E D L V
L Y I E O L A O T X B E E Z
E N O T S W O L L E Y G Z E
P I U M F M O E P N V G D D
A S X N I C V X E A M A Z N
H K M O U N T A I N R J R E
C R E S Y E G Y W T A K F R
```

1. ACCESSORY
2. BUSINESS CARD
3. CARTRIDGE
4. DOCUMENT
5. ELECTRICITY
6. FILM
7. FLASHCARDS
8. HEAT
9. KEEPSAKE
10. MACHINE
11. NAMETAG
12. OFFICE
13. PACK
14. PHOTO
15. POUCH
16. PRESERVATION
17. PROTECTOR
18. RIGIDITY
19. SCHOOL
20. SEALS
21. STRENGTH
22. THICKNESS
23. TWO-SIDED
24. WALLET SIZE
25. WIDENESS

```
E N I H C A M L O O H C S R
K M O W V E K A S P E E K O
B U S I N E S S C A R D F T
P Y G A T E M A N T S F M C
Y T T S E A L S W T I L W E
R I T I H K V O N C I A V T
O D L H C T S R E F L S U O
S I X A I I G S E L E H H R
S G P H D C R N E S Y C C P
E I Q E P A K T E N E A U H
C R D A F X S N C R E R O O
C A R T R I D G E E T D P T
A T T O Z F B M T S L S I O
W T N E M U C O D U S E I W
```

1. ANGORA

2. BEETS

3. BELGIAN HARE

4. BREAD

5. BROKEN-

    COLORED

6. CARROTS

7. CAULIFLOWER

8. DANDELIONS

9. DRINKING WATER

10. FLEMISH GIANT

11. FRESH GRASS

12. HAY

13. LETTUCE

14. LONG EARS

15. LOP-EARED

16. MANGEL-WURZEL

17. MILK

18. OATS

19. PLANTAIN

20. POLISH

21. RAW VEGETABLES

22. SOFT FUR

23. SWAMP

24. TURNIPS

```
S R K R L O P E A R E D P B
L E Z R U W L E G N A M R N
C T L E T T U C E N A O P F
A A R B R E A D D W K B L W
R W U Y A H S E S E G E A C
R G F L J T L R N H M L N I
O N T B I I E C A I A G T S
T I F D O F O G S E T I A X
S K O N P L L H E U G A I G
T N S G O O G O R V R N N M
E I O R I I L N W O W H O I
E R E A A I I I G E H A I L
B D O N T P D N S L R R R K
L R T U S S A R G H S E R F
```

1. ADHESION
2. APPLICATION
3. BEAD
4. CAP
5. CERAMIC
6. CHINA
7. CRAFT
8. DISPENSER
9. DROPS
10. FILLING
11. FIXER
12. GAP
13. GEL
14. GLASS
15. NO-CLOG
16. NOZZLE
17. OPENING
18. PAPER
19. PINPOINT
20. PRECISION
21. PROJECT
22. REPAIR
23. SQUEEZE
24. STRENGTH
25. TEXTILE
26. TRINKETS
27. TUBE
28. VINYL
29. VISCOSITY
30. WOOD

```
P B T P O V G P W S S A L G
N A G R I N K X A U Q L K O
G C G N I L L I F P U R A J
O U Y N C N R I A P E R O A
L L E Y W R K C M X E R D M
C P D T P O A E I N Z H C D
O P U I L R O F T L E G I E
N I R S A Y E D T S R S M L
O N N O I T A C I L P P A I
Z P N C J E D O I E L O R T
Z O G S B E N A N S A R E X
L I H I P C C S J L I D C E
E N A V P T E T U B E O X T
H T G N E R T S D C H I N A
```

1. ANIMALS
2. CHARACTER LINES
3. COLOR
4. COTTON
5. CRISPNESS
6. DESIGNS
7. DYE
8. FABRIC
9. FINISH
10. FLOWERS
11. FRUIT
12. HAND-BLOCKED
13. HEATED STEEL
14. MILLS
15. MOTIF
16. PATTERN
17. PEOPLE
18. PERIOD
19. PROTECTION
20. REMNANT
21. RESIN
22. SILK-SCREENED
23. SURFACE
24. TEXTILES
25. TINT
26. VICTORIAN
27. WAX
28. YARD

```
S E D S O S S E N P S I R C
V N L V U A F I N I S H H O
T N G P E R I O D U E A T T
V F O I O G F S V A R N C T
P I X I S E R A T A A D R O
J T C A T E P E C N N B N N
T O H T W C D T M E R L S I
E M S O O S E E B C E O B S
X A L L T R R T I N T C T E
T F O E L N I R O G T K D R
I R E I N I B A Y R A E C E
L L N S L A M I N A P D P E
E E C C F R U I T M R I Y G
S I L K S C R E E N E D Q W
```

6 EVERYDAY BEAUTY

1. BIRDS
2. BOOKS
3. BRIDGES
4. CANDLELIGHT
5. CHILDREN
6. COUNTRYSIDE
7. DAWN
8. FAMILY
9. FRIENDS
10. HOME
11. LAUGHTER
12. LEAVES
13. MOON
14. MOUNTAINS
15. MUSIC
16. NATURE

17. PETS
18. POETRY
19. PRAISE
20. QUIETUDE
21. RAINDROPS
22. SKY
23. SMILE
24. STARS
25. SUNSET
26. SUNSHINE
27. TRANQUILLITY
28. TREES
29. TWILIGHT
30. YOUTH

```
Z S U N S H I N E M O H E S
S P M U S I C I N A W Y N T
T O S I P L F T L Y Q Y B E
H R T N L Y R R K U T O R P
G D A F I E N S I H M U I D
I N R N E A U E G E T T D A
L I S S Q N T I R A N H G W
E A Y A S U L N N D E D E N
L R R E D I I B U S L G S O
D I T E W F R L I O K I X O
N R E T H G U A L R M O H M
A C O U N T R Y S I D E O C
C R P M M P A A M I T S C B
S E V A E L F A M I L Y W V
```

1. BRUSH
2. CARPET
3. CHEMICALS
4. CLEANING
5. DEODORIZER
6. DIRT
7. DRYING
8. FLOOR
9. FOAM
10. FORMULA
11. GUARANTEE
12. HALL
13. MACHINE
14. METHODS
15. PROFESSIONALS

16. PROTECTION
17. RATE
18. RINSE
19. ROOMS
20. SCRUBBING
21. SHAMPOO
22. SOAKING
23. SPOTS
24. SPRAY
25. STAINS
26. STEAM
27. TREATMENT
28. VACUUM

```
S H A M P O O M V L S T O T
L Y R F O R M U L A E N R S
A N S A R E S A A P C E A T
N T B N T E H C R N A U G E
O R C H I E Z A O T I S U A
I I O S L A C I M E H C A M
S D C O M Y T E R S F F R G
S L B L A C N S M O K S A N
E A L R E T I L A A D T N I
F E P T U A J M C K M O T Y
O S O I U S N A H I G P E R
R R O O L F H I I N C S E D
P S C R U B B I N G M F N D
S M O O R I N S E G A Y L B
```

1. AFTERNOON
2. APRON
3. CAMERA
4. CANDLES
5. CHAIR
6. CHEF
7. COOK
8. CROQUET
9. DANCE
10. DRINKS
11. EVENING
12. FOOD
13. FRIENDS
14. GRILL
15. GUESTS
16. HOT DOGS
17. INVITE
18. LAUGH
19. MUSIC
20. NEIGHBORS
21. POOL
22. RECORDS
23. SODA
24. STEAK
25. SWIM
26. TABLE
27. TALK
28. VISIT
29. WEEKEND
30. YARD

```
E I L G R I L L A U G H N I
I X O Q O D H F M T A L K H
C R O Q U E T S N I Y C T G
K S P Q O E G R Z S L A D I
U A D S R O B H G I E N R H
D Q E N D G A R S V E D C D
R F O T E N U R E K N L E A
I O O M S I U E E C L E C Z
N H I O I N R E S M O S N A
K W V S D E W F R T A R A J
S F E T I V N I A P S C D H
X D E T N E A B R H O D N S
E T N H C H L O K O D H M T
M U S I C E N D K K A M X N
```

9 THINGS WE READ

1. AGREEMENT

2. BIBLE

3. COMICS

4. DIRECTIONS

5. EDITORIAL

6. GREETING CARD

7. INSTRUCTIONS

8. LITERATURE

9. MAPS

10. MENU

11. MYSTERIES

12. NEWSPAPERS

13. NOTES

14. NOVELS

15. PAMPHLET

16. PAPERBACKS

17. PERIODICAL

18. POETRY

19. REFERENCES

20. SCHEDULE

21. TEXTBOOK

22. THERMOMETER

```
N Y S Z T P O E T R Y L Z Y
L P M N Q E L S P E I A T P
G E A L O B X E L T D N S A
S R L M I I L T E E Q E P
E I E B P U T R B M V C T E
I O L E D H A C E O O O O R
R D U E T T L E E M O T N B
E I H H U I R E I R E K E A
T C Y R L G N C T E I N X C
S A E F A F S G S H W D U K
Y L I N S T R U C T I O N S
M A P S N E W S P A P E R S
E S E C N E R E F E R Y V G
K P C S L A I R O T I D E J
```

1. BARGELLO
2. BYZANTINE
3. CASHMERE
4. CHAIN
5. DARNING
6. DOUBLE
7. EMBROIDERY
8. FERN
9. GOBELIN
10. GREEK
11. HERRINGBONE
12. KNITTING
13. KNOTTED
14. LEAF
15. LEVIATHAN
16. MILANESE
17. MOSAIC
18. OBLIQUE
19. OLD FLORENTINE
20. PERSPECTIVE
21. RAILWAY
22. RENAISSANCE
23. RICE
24. SMYRNA
25. STAR
26. STEM
27. TRIANGLE
28. WEB

```
T S G B F S E U Q I L B O D
H M N N A H T A I V E L A T
R Y I I E R S A N W D C E L
E R T H L T G D R F E M I V
N N T E E E A E L D B K T R
A A I M Y R B O L R O R D K
I X N T N A R O O L I G E C
S Z K I N E W I G A O E T A
S A N I N A D L N D R L T S
A G A T D E Z G I G E B O H
N H I H R D L Y Z A B U N M
C N H Y F E R N B E R O K E
E V I T C E P S R E P D N R
Z C I A S O M I L A N E S E
```

1. ABRASIVE

2. APPLIED

3. ARTISTIC

4. CARVED

5. COATING

6. DECORATIVE

7. DESIGN

8. DRYING

9. DYES

10. FINISHING

11. GLOSSY

12. GOLD

13. HARDENING

14. METALLIC

15. MOIST

16. OBJECTS

17. OXIDIZING

18. PIGMENTS

19. PROCESS

20. PRODUCTS

21. PROTECTIVE

22. QUALITY

23. RUBBING

24. RUST

25. SAP

26. SILVER

27. SURFACES

28. THIN

29. TRANSPARENT

```
M E T A L L I C D E V R A C
I P V M Y S I L V E R E H I
F G N I Z I D I X O S V Q L
Z I Z O S F T R U B B I N G
G T N E R A P S N A R T G M
N O I I R N R N U A N C S N
I B G O S I D B R R P E T V
N J C L T H Y T A A C T C S
E E C T O T I P S A D O U S
D C R Z I S P N F I A R D E
R T I L T L S R G T O P O C
A S A I I E U Y I Z R M R O
H U C E Y S T N E M G I P R
Q I D D L O G N I Y R D N P
```

1. BATTLE

2. BOOM

3. BUZZ

4. CLANG

5. CLAP

6. CRUNCH

7. DRONE

8. DRUMS

9. GARGLING

10. GRUMBLES

11. HUBBUB

12. JANGLE

13. RASP

14. REVERBERATION

15. SCREECH

16. SMACK

17. SNAPS

18. SPIEL

19. SWISH

20. THUD

21. THUNDER

22. TICK

23. UPROAR

J R G N A L C J H R O N N Z
W D H N M I O J A S L O V D
I K C B I N O O B N I Q S L
Z F E A H L R F P T G W Y U
W K E T N P G P A L C L S F
R I R T U F Y R S X M B E R
G A C L C P E C A C S B S D
I D S E L B M U R G P M R S
G R W P R R F E H U A O P M
C I X E Z T D Z G C N G K U
F X V B P N H Z K E S C O R
H E O H U B B U B H X U H D
R O P H P L V B D N Z X S L
M T T I C K P L E I P S D V

1. BRIAR
2. BUBBLE
3. CHIMNEY
4. CLAY
5. CONDUIT
6. COPPER
7. CORNCOB
8. CULVERT
9. DRAIN
10. DRIP
11. DUCT
12. EXHAUST
13. FLUE
14. HEATING
15. HOLLOW
16. HORN
17. HYDRANT
18. LEAD
19. LEAKY
20. METAL
21. PITCH
22. SINK
23. SOLDERED
24. STOVE
25. SUCTION
26. TAIL
27. VENT
28. WASTE
29. WATER
30. WIND

```
R D R L G S M K C K B H Z B
T R E V L U C E N V F L U E
L A T D R I P I T C H B P B
D I A V E A S C M A B H R H
E R W H Y R O H O L L O W Q
L B O X E R E Z E N B R V T
U O B T N A R D Y H D N S S
T Y J C M N T N L K L U R U
M C O U I D R I A O A K I C
L B U A H N E W N H S E Z T
R I R D C V P V X G I N L I
Y D A F O S P E T S A W N O
R I X T O R O N X N Z Z O N
B H S Y A L C T U G T Q M L
```

14 SING THE BLUES

1. AQUA
2. AZURE
3. CADET
4. CELESTIAL
5. CERULEAN
6. COBALT
7. COPENHAGEN
8. DARK
9. DENIM
10. FADED
11. FEDERAL
12. FRENCH
13. INDIGO
14. LAPIS LAZULI
15. LIGHT
16. LUPINE
17. MARINE
18. MIDNIGHT
19. NAVY
20. PERIWINKLE
21. ROYAL
22. SAPPHIRE
23. SKY
24. SLATE
25. SPRUCE
26. TEAL
27. TURQUOISE
28. WEDGWOOD

```
H L J Z B N A E L U R E C G
H A Z U R E T A L S O T E I
C X E M I D N I G H T L L L
N P H C B O G I D N I U E B
E L E V U T X E R T Z L S F
R R E R L R N F U A A U T J
F D I A I I P R L R M P I A
D O B H M W Q S E O T I A J
C O X W P U I D G Y H N L F
C W F C O P E N H A G E N D
H G C I A F A N K L I B L K
M D S L U D A S R L L A I R
L E Y K F V E F A D E D M C
Y W L D Y B J T D T A U Q A
```

1. ARMOIRE	19. LOVE SEAT
2. BENCH	20. MATTRESS
3. BOOKCASE	21. MIRROR
4. BUREAU	22. OTTOMAN
5. CABINET	23. PANS
6. CARPET	24. PERCOLATOR
7. CHEST	25. POTS
8. CHINA	26. RADIO
9. CLOCK	27. SETTEE
10. CONSOLE	28. SHADES
11. CRIB	29. SHELVES
12. CURTAINS	30. SOFA
13. DESK	31. STEREO
14. DIVAN	32. STOOL
15. DRESSER	33. TABLE
16. HAMPER	34. TELEVISION
17. HASSOCK	35. WARDROBE
18. LAMP	

```
N E L B A T L P M A L H S P
O R E P M A H W A A C T O K
I D R T E C A B I N E T S C
S N I A T R U C E R S S O O
I N Q V D E C B E R H I F L
V L C R A I S O T E P R A C
E T O B H N O K L M T N R H
L B B O O R C V U A U A M I
E S U M T O E M E T T M O N
T E R R S S K S I T A O I A
E D E S N S E C S R Z T R C
H A A J E V M H A E R T E T
E H U D O B I R C S R O J A
Y S E L O S N O C S E D R K
```

1. CAIMAN
2. CAMEL
3. CANINE
4. CAPON
5. CAPUCHIN
6. CARDINAL
7. CASSOWARY
8. CAT
9. CAYUSE
10. CHAFFINCH
11. CHAMOIS
12. CHANTICLEER
13. CHICKADEE
14. CHICKEN
15. CHIMPANZEE
16. CHINCHILLA
17. CHOW
18. CLAM
19. CLYDESDALE
20. COATI
21. COLLIE
22. COLT
23. CONCH
24. CORGI
25. COTTONTAIL
26. COW
27. CRAB
28. CRANE
29. CRAWFISH
30. CROCODILE
31. CROW
32. CYGNET

```
R M I G R O C O A T I D L D
E A C F C H I M P A N Z E E
E L H E O C C L L E F Y M L
L C A W E O R L O C N R A I
C Y M D L D I A O H C A C D
I G O L S H A T W A D W R O
T N I W C E T K P F D O O C
N E S N O O D U C F I S W O
A T I C N C C Y X I B S K R
H H O T A H Z L L N H A H C
C L A N I D R A C C O C R T
T I I N N E K C I H C P A C
L N A M I A C A Y U S E A T
E G R F D V X V R H C N O C
```

1. AIRCRAFT
2. AIRFLOW
3. AIR RACING
4. AMATEUR
5. AVIATION
6. CATEGORY
7. CHALLENGE
8. CONTEST
9. CONTROL
10. CREW
11. ENTRIES
12. FLYING
13. GOAL
14. GOGGLES
15. HEIGHT
16. JUMPING
17. LOOPS

18. MEET
19. MOTOR
20. PERFORM
21. PILOT
22. POWER ENGINES
23. PROFESSION
24. RACES
25. RANGE
26. ROLL
27. RULES
28. STUNTS
29. STYLE
30. TEAM
31. TIMING
32. TRAINERS

```
T S T U N T S P O O L S G R
E F L R U E T A M A E N Y R
E P A O I L S R E N I A R T
M W R R R E X K I Y E I O S
H R T O C T Y G L Q A R G E
S N O A F R N F Q V I F E T
E R R F E E I O I Z R L T N
L R M L R L S A C R R O A O
U O Y E T E T S H Z A W C C
R T W E L I P W I E C N N O
S O A G O L L O R O I R G S
P M G N C H A L L E N G E E
G O A L J U M P I N G Y H W
G N I M I T R B J P I L O T
```

1. ALABASTER

2. CANVAS

3. CARDIGAN

4. CASHMERE

5. CERAMICS

6. CLOCK

7. CLOGS

8. CORK PRODUCTS

9. CRYSTAL

10. ENAMELED SILVER

11. KILT

12. LACES

13. LINENS

14. MANTILLA

15. OILS

16. PEARLS

17. PIPE

18. PORCELAIN

19. STERLING

20. SUEDE

21. SWEATERS

22. TAM

23. TARTANS

24. THISTLE GLASS

25. TWEED

26. WATCH

27. WOODCARVINGS

```
R R D E E W T A R T A N S P
L E C A S H M E R E H M S P
A V T O L D A L L I T N A M
C L L S R Y S C K V Z G L T
E I I J A K N G A P G L G J
S S K R E B P N O N X L E S
C D Y S P J A R I L V T L W
I E J I N G C L O W C A T E
M L P D I E R L A D T B S A
A E A D L E N T O S U L I T
R M R A T V C I Y C I C H E
E A I S M H H R L O K Y T R
C N W O O D C A R V I N G S
O E D E U S Z A J S O O D F
```

1. GARLAND
2. GAUD
3. GELID
4. GERUND
5. GHOST-WEED
6. GIFTED
7. GILD
8. GINGERBREAD
9. GIRD
10. GIRLFRIEND
11. GIZZARD
12. GLAD
13. GOAD
14. GODCHILD
15. GODSEND

16. GOLDENROD
17. GOOD
18. GOURD
19. GOURMAND
20. GRANDCHILD
21. GRANDSTAND
22. GRASSLAND
23. GREED
24. GREYHOUND
25. GRID
26. GRIND
27. GROUND
28. GUARD
29. GUILD

```
D G E R U N D I R G Y S T F
E U R G G R E Y H O U N D B
T A D E E W T S O H G O W D
F R G N E L S D C D R G E N
I D I O A D I G R N R N C A
G A R I O T O D E A D K P M
A G L A D D S D N L Z N I R
R I F N C C L D I S X Z D U
L G R H A O C U N S G N I O
A K I R G H G M H A I T D G
N L E R I O L B U R R L A G
D A N L D O U D G G I G O I
Y W D A E R B R E G N I G O
Z D N U O R G O D S E N D D
```

1. ALMENDRA
2. AMALUZA
3. CHIRLEY
4. CONTRA
5. DARTMOUTH
6. DWORSHAK
7. EMOSSON
8. HAIPU
9. KARAKAYA
10. KEBAN
11. KINSHAU
12. LAKHWAR
13. LOS LEONES
14. LUZZONE
15. MICA
16. MIHOESTI
17. MOSSYROCK
18. MRATINJE
19. NADER SHAH
20. NUREK
21. OYMOPINAR
22. SAN ROGUE
23. SHASTA
24. TACHIEN
25. TAKASE
26. TIGNES
27. TOKTOGUL
28. VAIONT
29. VIDRARU

```
U N A B E K C O R Y S S O M
R T A K A S E E X A E Q U N
A L H U A R M R R L N Y A C
R U A Y A O A D U E O D C S
D Z T K S H N N J N E D H X
I Z N S H E S N I R L A I K
V O O T M W I N S P S R R A
S N I L O T A H I T O T L H
E E A Y A K A R A K L M E S
N U V R M H T B I Q Y O Y R
G P M I T S E O H I M U A O
I I C S A N R O G U E T S W
T A C H I E N Y S U R H Y D
Z H C O N T R A M A L U Z A
```

21 COWBOY BOOT JEWELRY

1. ALL SIZES
2. ANKLE
3. ANTIQUES
4. BRACELETS
5. BUTTONS
6. CHARMS
7. CLASPS
8. COPPER
9. COSTLY
10. CRAFTS
11. CREATIVE
12. DESIGNS
13. DIFFERENT
14. EMBELLISHMENT
15. FAD
16. FOOTWEAR
17. GOLD
18. HEELS
19. INDUSTRY
20. MEDALLIONS
21. ORNAMENTS
22. PEARLS
23. PINS
24. PORCELAIN
25. SHOP
26. SILVER
27. STONES
28. TOECAPS

```
T N E M H S I L L E B M E S
W J R H X N U C H A R M S G
R A E W T O O F F V A H K W
Q S V Y G I C A O B C P E S
B T L N I L L R F O E S L A
U F I V I L N I E A L E K R
T A S Q S A N W R A E U N C
T R D I M D L L S H T Q A O
O C Z E U E S E K T S I T P
N E N S S M P C C I O T V P
S T T G D I F F E R E N T E
S R O L N A G R N U O A E R
Y L T S O C F N S H O P I S
D N T O E C A P S P S A L C
```

1. CARVE
2. CHIP
3. CHISEL
4. CHOP
5. CLEAVE
6. CROP
7. CUBE
8. ENGRAVE
9. GRATE
10. INCISE
11. INSCRIBE
12. INTERSECT
13. JULIENNE
14. LANCE
15. MACERATE
16. MINCE
17. PARE
18. PEEL
19. PLANE
20. PRUNE
21. SCISSOR
22. SCULPT
23. SHAPE
24. SHAVE
25. SHEAR
26. SLICE
27. SLIVER
28. SNIP
29. SPLIT
30. TRIM

```
N K E T A R E C A M B E J Y
S M Y R P V S B E R A P N M
H H A E A E E C I L S A H F
A A E R V C V N I R X H U I
V L G A U B T P H S C S R J
E N E B R E U P O Q S S U U
E L E V R A C S L H U O N L
C H I S E L D V P U C E R I
R Y E P M P E I W L C M E E
E C F L L E S I C N I S V N
T R I M N A S G A N V T I N
A O F U Z G N L C H I P L E
R P R N O B I E D U X Q S V
G P T I N U P J H N G L P F
```

1. AMSTERDAM

2. BERLIN

3. BERN

4. BRAUNFELS

5. BRIGHTON

6. CALEDONIA

7. CARROLLTON

8. CASTILE

9. CITY

10. FAIRFIELD

11. FOREST

12. FRANCE

13. GRANADA

14. HAMPSHIRE

15. HARMONY

16. IRELAND

17. KENSINGTON

18. NETHERLAND

19. PHILADELPHIA

20. PLYMOUTH

21. PROVIDENCE

22. SOUTH WALES

23. SPAIN

24. WESTMINSTER

25. YORK

```
P L Y M O U T H A R M O N Y
I H J D R X F S M J B E R N
A N I I N R Q A E R J R B D
S I K L A A D G I R E G P L
L L N N A R L G R T O D R E
E R C O E D H R S A N F O I
F E N T D T E N E A N V V F
N B S G O E I L L H P A I R
U M G N N M L E P Y T Y D I
A O R I T O R A T H T E E A
R C A S T I L E C M I I N F
B P E N O T L L O R R A C D
S W S E L A W H T U O S E T
Y O R K E R I H S P M A H U
```

1. BISCUIT
2. BLISTER
3. BLUNGER
4. CRACKLE
5. CROCKERY
6. DELFT
7. DRESDEN
8. FAIENCE
9. FRIT
10. GLAZE
11. KAOLIN
12. KILN
13. MAJOLICA
14. MING
15. NANKIN
16. OXIDATION
17. PALLET
18. PARIAN
19. PORCELAIN
20. POTSHERD
21. POTTERY
22. PUG MILL
23. SGRAFFITO
24. SIEVE
25. SLIP
26. SLURRY
27. SPODE
28. THROWING
29. WARE
30. WASH
31. WEDGWOOD

```
W D E E P B B H S A W Q Y F
E E R V D O S G L A Z E R D
D L A E M O R B L U N G E R
G F W I H A P C T P N Z K E
W T N S F S J S E I R R C S
O G G F R P T T W L R M O D
O X I D A T I O N S A F R E
D T P R G U R N P J P I C N
O S I O C H I E O N U A N L
I A L S T L A L T G G B W I
N S I U O T I Q V S M H Y K
V B S A R C E C N E I A F I
E L K C A R C R T E L L A P
N I K N A N Y R Y E L L B X
```

1. BABY-SITTER
2. BAND
3. BARTENDER
4. BELLBOY
5. BUTLER
6. CABDRIVER
7. CATERER
8. CHAUFFEUR
9. CONCIERGE
10. DOORMAN
11. HELPER
12. HOSTESS
13. MAID

14. MANICURIST
15. MESSENGER
16. NANNY
17. PAPERBOY
18. PIANO PLAYER
19. PIZZA DELIVERY
20. REDCAP
21. REPAIRMAN
22. SHAMPOOER
23. STEWARD
24. VALET

```
G C I M R E V I R D B A C U
X B A R T E N D E R D W O V
Y I A T R E P A I R M A N J
D O I B E E B A N D D X C J
P S B Z Y R O H C O Z M I R
A S U L A S E O O D A U E U
P E T F L L I R P N E G R E
E T L T P E M T I M N R G F
R S E E O A B C T E A Y E F
B O R L N Z U P S E N H F U
O H G A A R F S B N R Q S A
Y R E V I L E D A Z Z I P H
W F Z S P M F N G U K Y K C
N S T E W A R D R W A A N Q
```

1. BOTTLE
2. BUTTER
3. CAN
4. CARTON
5. COLD
6. COWS
7. CREAM
8. DAIRY
9. GALLON
10. GLASS
11. GOAT
12. HOMOGENIZED
13. ICED
14. LACTOSE

15. MILK
16. PAIL
17. PASTEURIZED
18. PINT
19. POWDERED
20. PUMP
21. QUART
22. RICH
23. SKIM
24. SOUR
25. VATS
26. WHOLE
27. YOGURT

```
C V A J S A S Q V V Y U I H
D K V P R G U M P L A Z D D
S L H R P A I L J M X T E O
O I C O R L J P O Z U Z S C
U M H T M L Y N A C I P O C
R E L T T O B M G R R W T K
F E N Z G N G E U T S E C I
N I T U O O Y E J B T W A G
P J R T A H T R N T Y H L M
D T R T U S C G I I Z O D M
E A X G A B W I U A Z L M L
C Z P P O W D E R E D E Y M
I P A K K I R D G C O L D U
G M F L M I K S S A L G E O
```

1. ABILITY
2. APPLAUSE
3. DEXTERITY
4. ELBOWING
5. FALLS
6. JOSTLING
7. LAPS
8. MATCH
9. OPPONENTS
10. OVAL TRACK
11. PASSING
12. PERIODS
13. PLAYERS
14. POINTS
15. RINK
16. RIVALS
17. ROLLER SKATES
18. SIDES
19. SKILL
20. SPECTATORS
21. SPEED
22. SPORT
23. TEAMS
24. TOUGH
25. TRIPPING
26. TUMBLES
27. UNIFORMS

D	Z	L	A	A	B	I	L	I	T	Y	F	Z	G
L	O	D	S	E	D	I	S	P	E	E	D	T	J
L	P	A	E	L	B	O	W	I	N	G	A	U	S
I	P	B	T	X	L	I	N	H	C	T	A	M	Y
K	O	V	A	L	T	R	A	C	K	S	R	B	S
S	N	Z	K	U	A	E	L	N	P	O	P	L	Q
G	E	I	S	H	P	U	R	E	F	E	U	E	P
N	N	Z	R	G	P	G	C	I	R	A	H	S	S
I	T	I	E	U	L	T	N	I	T	S	L	L	B
P	S	S	L	O	A	U	O	I	T	Y	A	L	S
P	F	P	L	T	U	D	D	N	S	V	B	J	S
I	P	O	O	F	S	M	I	P	I	S	V	P	W
R	L	R	R	A	E	O	S	R	E	Y	A	L	P
T	S	T	Y	T	P	L	J	D	E	L	P	P	P

1. APPLE CRISP

2. BEIGNET

3. BOMBE

4. BROWNIE

5. CAKE

6. CHEESE

7. CHERRIES

8. COOKIES

9. CREME BRULEE

10. CUSTARD

11. FONDUE

12. ICE CREAM

13. KEY LIME PIE

14. MADELEINES

15. PARFAIT

16. PASTRY

17. PEACHES

18. PEARS

19. PETIT FOURS

20. PUDDING

21. SHERBET

22. SORBET

23. SUNDAE

24. TART

I	T	A	R	T	P	U	D	D	I	N	G	E	C
S	E	H	C	A	E	P	C	C	Z	B	E	E	M
I	N	R	N	G	D	O	E	I	O	F	A	L	R
K	G	C	X	K	O	C	K	M	O	R	D	U	S
P	I	E	H	K	R	W	B	N	M	P	N	R	H
S	E	N	I	E	L	E	D	A	M	B	U	B	E
I	B	E	A	P	R	U	C	J	L	O	S	E	R
R	S	M	P	M	E	R	E	U	F	E	T	M	B
C	K	S	A	Q	C	M	I	T	S	D	A	E	E
E	T	B	R	O	W	N	I	E	E	T	G	R	T
L	P	E	F	A	Z	T	E	L	S	B	A	C	P
P	N	T	A	O	E	H	D	K	Y	G	R	R	R
P	L	O	I	P	C	P	B	J	A	E	J	O	D
A	Y	R	T	S	A	P	F	E	D	C	K	C	S

1. ACCESS
2. ALARM
3. ARCHWAY
4. BACK
5. BELL
6. ENTRY
7. EXIT
8. FIRE
9. FOLDING
10. FRAME
11. FRONT
12. GLASS
13. HINGE
14. HOOK
15. JAMB
16. KEY
17. KNOB
18. LATCH
19. LOCK
20. MAIN
21. METAL
22. OPEN
23. PASSAGE
24. PORCH
25. REVOLVING
26. SCREEN
27. SILL
28. SLIDING
29. STOP
30. WOODEN

```
S M I F E E W O O P Q W D S
P A E S N R S W K B E L L S
F I O T S S I J C G S I L L
R N R B A E E F O L D I N G
P Y M L R L C G L I B O N K
E A G X C N U C N Y B I E L
J W S E H Q E G A I V N D U
W Z X S W M U P D L H N O T
Y I F I A H C R O P M C O N
T E V R Y G W V L L R H W O
B R F H N E E R C S A L K R
Y A S O U R H C T A L G Z F
A W C O D F A O B H A Y E K
U A A K Y K P W Q X L E S Z
```

1. BALK
2. BARRIER
3. BLOCKADE
4. BRAKE
5. CHECK
6. CLAMP
7. CLASP
8. CLIP
9. CORRAL
10. COVER
11. CRATE
12. CURB
13. DELAY
14. DODGE
15. FENCE
16. FORT

17. GATE
18. HEDGE
19. HITCH
20. LIMIT
21. OBSTACLE
22. REEL
23. REIN
24. ROPE
25. SHACKLE
26. SNAG
27. SNARE
28. STOP
29. STRAP
30. VETO

```
T  T  M  M  F  J  R  E  E  L  E  K  W  R
P  I  L  C  Y  A  L  E  D  M  C  U  O  E
Z  M  C  B  U  J  T  H  I  E  N  P  T  Q
U  I  L  B  P  A  O  I  H  N  E  S  E  Y
Y  L  A  R  R  O  C  C  Y  C  F  Y  V  J
Q  Y  S  C  E  A  T  P  A  R  T  S  W  A
O  Z  P  N  P  I  K  S  E  M  H  I  G  T
E  O  T  C  A  H  R  E  L  A  C  K  H  G
M  W  R  T  A  R  V  R  C  L  H  E  A  A
P  C  O  V  E  R  E  K  A  D  P  C  C  N
G  H  F  H  G  G  L  M  T  B  U  Q  S  S
B  A  L  K  D  E  P  P  S  R  I  Y  X  B
C  D  T  E  O  U  E  V  B  B  B  O  E  Y
Y  M  H  E  D  A  K  C  O  L  B  T  G  C
```

1. BOARDWALK

2. BUNGALOWS

3. CAMPFIRES

4. CANOES

5. DRIFTWOOD

6. FAMILIES

7. FIREWORKS

8. FRIENDS

9. NATURE

10. PICNICS

11. PICTURES

12. RACES

13. RAFTS

14. RELAXATION

15. SAILING

16. SANDCASTLES

17. SNACKS

18. SNORKELING

19. SPLASHING

20. SURFING

21. SWIMMING

22. VOLLEYBALL

23. WADING

```
Q J F I R E W O R K S C D S
D R I F T W O O D L E A N T
S E I L I M A F L A R N W F
S L G N I L I A S W U O S A
C A K S F A B N C D T E L R
I X N S W Y K E S R C S Z K
N A Z D E O F P S A I N S K
C T U L C R L W R O P A U Y
I I L Z I A I A A B B C R B
P O I E S M S F G D F K F F
V N N H M E S T P N I S I G
V D I I H N N G L M U N N X
S N N L N A T U R E A B G V
G G N I L E K R O N S C K J
```

1. AMUR
2. ARAGUAYA
3. ARKANSAS
4. CHANG JIANG
5. CONGO
6. DANUBE
7. INDUS
8. IRTYSH
9. LENA
10. MACKENZIE
11. MADEIRA
12. MEKONG
13. MISSOURI
14. MURRAY
15. NILE
16. ORINOCO
17. PARAGUAY
18. PARANA
19. PURUS
20. RIO GRANDE
21. SALWEEN
22. ST. LAWRENCE
23. SYR DARYA
24. TOCANTINS
25. VOLGA
26. YENISEI
27. YUKON

```
H S Y T R I R M P A R A N A
G Z W A M I S S O U R I K R
N S W L R E Y G J A I G C K
A E C N E R W A L T S S E A
I R Y X D A U O W K J U I N
J B A A R Y G M R P Z D Z S
G T R G U U B L I I O N N A
N Y H K U G M S O L N I E S
A I O E N A A A G V T O K X
H N L O D L Y R R N O P C N
C K K E W E P A A G V U A O
L E I E M N A C N P Z R M X
M R E P P A O O D A N U B E
A N V A P T C Y E N I S E I
```

1. BEDTIME
2. BLANKET
3. CANDLE
4. DARKNESS
5. DOZE
6. DREAM
7. DROWSE
8. DUSK
9. EVENING
10. GOWN
11. LAMP
12. MOON
13. NOISES
14. OWLS

15. PEACE
16. REPOSE
17. REST
18. ROBE
19. SILENCE
20. SLEEP
21. SLUMBER
22. STARS
23. TOSS
24. TRANQUILITY
25. TWILIGHT
26. VESPERS
27. YAWN

```
R L Z E T B B P N G I P I Q
C E L D N A C T E H M A E T
I S S N S B C Q E A E N R H
A O S T E E K Q L K C A I K
M P X E B D D A R K N E S S
S E V O S T O S S Q E A G U
V R R Z P I W N U Q L N L D
F P A H P M O I D S I T D B
T E B T K E L N L N S R O G
R E E R S I R U E I O W Z V
S L W O T K M V Y W G N E R
R S F Y A B E P S A O H T S
O H S R E P S E V O W Z T Z
Z P D R E A M S M K N N F O
```

1. BONHEUR
2. CEZANNE
3. COROT
4. DALI
5. DA VINCI
6. DEGAS
7. DELACROIX
8. DINE
9. DURER
10. EL GRECO
11. GAINSBOROUGH
12. GRANDMA MOSES
13. LAUTREC
14. MANET
15. MICHELANGELO
16. MIRO

17. MONET
18. PICASSO
19. REMBRANDT
20. REMINGTON
21. RENOIR
22. ROCKWELL
23. RUBENS
24. SHAHN
25. SLOAN
26. UTRILLO
27. VAN GOGH
28. VELAZQUEZ
29. VERMEER
30. WHISTLER

```
S E S O M A M D N A R G N S
E D A L I C N I V A D H O N
S V R O C K W E L L A V A O
N T S T H T V O U H E O R D
E D U R E R O R S L L U E E
B N S V L E I R A S E L L G
U A O R A O U Z O H A A T A
R R C T N N Q T N C U C S S
E B E E G U G O R T E N I D
E M R H E N B O R I E I H P
M E G Z L Z I E G I L N W G
R R L S O X C M V H M L A K
E C E Z A N N E E T E N O M
V P G A I N S B O R O U G H
```

1. AMBLE	17. SKIP
2. BEND	18. SPRINT
3. CLIMB	19. STEP
4. DANCE	20. STRETCH
5. GESTURE	21. STROLL
6. HOP	22. SWAY
7. JUMP	23. SWIM
8. KICK	24. SWING
9. LIFT	25. THROW
10. NOD	26. TURN
11. PULL	27. TWIST
12. REACH	28. WALK
13. RISE	29. WAVE
14. RUN	30. WIGGLE
15. SHAKE	
16. SHRUG	

```
D R G K H L Z C S T E P R W
A G L P Y S W I M C S P M S
D A S B U U P O R P K I C K
W R B M I L C P R I S K W I
R Q M H O V L I Z H S S L T
H U B O C Z N T A J T E L R
D V V S V T A K T W L X O E
R I D P U M E L G G I W R A
C U O R U A P R B J F U T C
S H N E H M M I T O T W S H
S W D N E B U E I S P H W Y
H W I V I L J F E T R D A P
U D A N C E A G T U N S L E
H W K Y G R F E G D J I U Q
```

1. ASHES

2. ATOM

3. BALSA

4. CHALK

5. CHIP

6. COBWEB

7. CORK

8. DUST

9. GRAM

10. HAIR

11. LINT

12. MIST

13. NEEDLE

14. PEANUT

15. PETAL

16. POPCORN

17. SEEDS

18. SNOWFLAKE

19. SPONGE

20. STAMP

21. STAPLE

22. STRAW

23. TACK

24. TISSUE

25. TOOTHPICK

```
J D U Y S Q E X Z M H J X Y
X D S S D P K L A H C F K E
M P T H E N K R D X P G E J
V H R T E S G E X E B M W K
Q Q A N S Y Q G A R E N O T
K L W R B J F N C Q E N H A
J C B O R A U O D U S T J C
R W I C K T L P S C L S H K
S U N P M A T S R J L I K F
M T A O H N I G A I P M N S
Q O A P A T A R Z Q A O E T
C X T P R C O R K K A H Y I
K E K A L F W O N S S E A P
H C O B W E B W T A J R Y O
```

1. COVER
2. CUE BID
3. CUT
4. DECEPTIVE PLAY
5. DECLARE
6. DISCARD
7. DOUBLE
8. ECHO
9. ENDPLAY
10. FINESSE
11. FORCE
12. GAME
13. GRAND SLAM
14. HONORS
15. JUMP BID
16. LEAD

17. MAJOR
18. MINOR
19. NO-TRUMP
20. OPENER
21. REBID
22. RUBBER
23. RULES
24. SACRIFICE
25. SCORE
26. SEQUENCE
27. SIGNAL
28. SINGLETON
29. SQUEEZE PLAY
30. SUIT
31. VALUE

```
D S L A N G I S N D G G A I
Y M I N O R S J O A A P E N
C A Q N O T R U M P Y E U L
N O L H G E B E I A T G L B
E J V P N L H O L T R S A Q
S Q U E E Z E P L A Y A V M
S B P M R V D T N L S C S Q
E O D B P N I D O M C R E E
N R R I E B S T A N O I L C
I U A T B L I J P N R F U R
F B C L A E O D O E E I R O
C B S M C R R H T U C C N F
U E I Q O E C N E U Q E S B
S R D N E E D I B E U C D Q
```

1. ANTIQUES
2. APPLIANCE
3. BICYCLE
4. BOOKS
5. CAMERA
6. CARRIAGE
7. CHEST
8. CLOCK
9. CLOTHES
10. COMICS
11. DESK
12. DISHES
13. DOLLS
14. DRESSER
15. DRILL
16. FANS

17. IRON
18. LAMP
19. PANS
20. PICTURE
21. ROCKER
22. SKATES
23. SLED
24. SOFA
25. STEREO
26. TABLE
27. TAPES
28. TIRES
29. TOASTER
30. TYPEWRITER

```
R S K O O B B D S I Y R G G
E K E G A I R R A C H E S T
T S U M C O E A N K I J D S
I E W Y C I T H T M C M C D
R D C K A N S H I X S O O X
W L E N T F A A Q L E L L C
E R Y P A B O E U R L T E C
P D W A B I T S E S R C N D
Y I I N L E L T S E T A K S
T L C S E C S P S L A M P S
C L O T H E S S P E Y E E S
G I I Y U E E T R A P R N R
J R K I D R S N O R I A Y C
L D P H D X E L K T F T T B
```

1. ANTIETAM

2. BASS

3. CHESAPEAKE BAY

4. CLAMS

5. CORN

6. CROSSLAND

7. CUMBERLAND

8. EASTERN SHORE

9. ELECTRONICS

10. FISHING

11. FORT MCHENRY

12. LIMESTONE

13. MARBLE

14. METALS

15. OLD LINE STATE

16. ORIOLE

17. OYSTERS

18. PERCH

19. PINE

20. POULTRY

21. RAYON

22. SALISBURY

23. SAND

24. SHAD

25. SUSQUEHANNA

26. WASHINGTON, D.C.

27. WHITE OAK

```
Y A B E K A E P A S E H C O
R E C U M B E R L A N D Y M
N N R O C R M S J C N J E G
E L O O C G S L B O L T L N
H K S H H A C Y T Z A A I I
C A S F B S I G R L N Y M H
M O L D L I N E S T A T E S
T E A A M I O R I O L E S I
R T N H H Y R E E P S U T F
O I D S S U T A L T I A O P
F H A T X A C T Y B S N N P
W W E E M V E A Q O R A E D
Y R U B S I L A S J N A E C
S S U S Q U E H A N N A M B
```

1. BOUNDER
2. BRAGGART
3. BUSYBODY
4. CHEATER
5. COWARD
6. CROOK
7. DRIFTER
8. FAWNER
9. FIBBER
10. FOOL
11. GLUTTON
12. HEEL
13. HOODLUM
14. KNAVE
15. LIAR

16. MISER
17. RASCAL
18. ROGUE
19. ROTTER
20. SHYSTER
21. SINNER
22. SNEAK
23. SNOB
24. SOT
25. SPONGER
26. THUG
27. TRAITOR
28. VANDAL
29. VILLAIN

```
R R C X G I Q Z M I S E R I
R E B B I F H S C K A E N S
X N T D A O B R A R N L W X
C N Y F O Z O E E W O Y R H
T I F D I O U G A O T O I E
G S L X K R N F F E T G E E
B U S Y B O D Y U T U O Y L
M R R C P T E W E H L G S I
R E A S O P R R T A G N O A
H T S G E W V A N D A L E R
B S C N G V A V I L L A I N
Y Y A K O A A R E T A E H C
S H L V W B R N D M O J W F
G S W X U U P T K W L R E Q
```

1. BASIL
2. CELERY
3. CHEESE
4. COOL
5. CRISP
6. CUCUMBER
7. DRESSING
8. EGG
9. FRESH
10. FRUIT
11. GARLIC
12. ICEBERG
13. LEAF
14. LEMON
15. LETTUCE
16. MAYONNAISE

17. MELON
18. MINCE
19. MINT
20. OLIVE
21. ONION
22. PEAS
23. PEPPER
24. RADISH
25. SALAD OIL
26. SALMON
27. SALT
28. SLICE
29. SPINACH
30. TOMATO

```
E N H D X X I Q F Z O F F X
S I D L E A F R U I T P G K
I C R R K C E L I S A B A P
A E S D E S T W I V M S R I
N B A L H S A L A D O I L J
N E E L A M S C A A T R I C
O R P H C A N I P S E W C I
Y G P N J E B O N B V X C X
A H G S L I C E M G T P O E
M G S H I H K U Z E E U O V
E I M I E R C Z T P L N L I
L Z N E D U C N P T I Y V L
O U S C C A I E J O E N Y O
N E E E E M R K N O M L A S
```

1. ALCHEMY

2. ALLOY

3. BEAUTY

4. CERTIFICATES

5. COINS

6. DUST

7. ELEMENT

8. FORT KNOX

9. GILT

10. GRADE

11. INGOT

12. INVESTMENT

13. KARATS

14. LEAF

15. LODE

16. METAL

17. MINT

18. PRECIOUS

19. RESERVE

20. RUSH

21. SOFT

22. STANDARD

23. TRADE

24. VEIN

25. WHITE

26. YELLOW

```
O Y B E A U T Y Y R Y X J E
I Y N D S F E A L L O Y V X
S N R O E L E M E N T H W G
G E G L L V S D K V R R S W
T C T O R S R T A Q M U H T
Q H W A T U R E A R S I S Q
H E E L C O L M S N T U Y H
Z E G C F I V W I E D L Y X
G G W H K C F O N Q R A U B
I K O E A E C I S O F T R P
L H C M R R T P T N I E V D
T E I Y A P E D A R G M U N
X N A D T N E M T S E V N I
T L Y F S V A Z W O N C S J
```

1. ADDRESS
2. ADMIT
3. ADVISE
4. ARGUE
5. ARTICULATE
6. AVOW
7. BANTER
8. BLAB
9. CHAT
10. CLAIM
11. CLARIFY
12. DEBATE
13. DISCUSS
14. DISPUTE
15. ENCOURAGE
16. EXPLAIN

17. EXPRESS
18. GREET
19. ORATE
20. PLEAD
21. PREACH
22. PRONOUNCE
23. RECITE
24. RECOMMEND
25. TELL
26. TRANSLATE
27. UTTER
28. VENT
29. VERBALIZE
30. WARN

```
O B E X P L A I N V E L M N
X A Z T A I D T Z C T H G P
Z L I E A R E I C L A I M R
E B L E R L T S S E R P X E
T X A R L R S I C C O P U A
U C B G E E N C D U W Q C
P S R A S C U T A U A S E H
S I E I B O I A T R L E S C
I S V Y N M D T N U T A L S
D D E O X M T N E V E A T P
A Y R R I E N C O U R A G E
L P S T D N T K G I H V N S
E T A B E D I R F C Z O Z T
R E T N A B A Y C K R W Z R
```

1. ANGUS

2. AUROCHS

3. BEEF

4. BISON

5. BOSSY

6. BOVINE

7. BRAND

8. BUFFALO

9. BULL

10. CALF

11. CATTLE

12. CHAMPION

13. FENCE

14. GUERNSEY

15. HEIFER

16. HERD

17. HEREFORD

18. HOLSTEIN

19. HOOF

20. LIVESTOCK

21. LONGHORN

22. OXEN

23. PUREBRED

24. SHORTHORN

25. STEER

26. VEAL

27. ZEBU

```
R G D C T B C D E B H B O G
E M S H C O R U A R R O A H
F Y G H E B Y D Z V E A L E
I N K C O T S E V I L E N R
E Q N V F R B O S S Y H X D
H E I E F U T L P N N E X O
F N E Y O T G H O D R R L P
E B I S O N O I O E C E S J
C L F B H L P S W R R F U I
E R T L S M A K T B N O G G
D B Y T A Y V F U E M R N P
H W E H A C B L F R E D A X
O I C S X C L N P U G R O U
N N R O H G N O L P B D X F
```

1. ANKLE LENGTH
2. APPAREL
3. BELT LOOP
4. BIAS
5. DARTS
6. DESIGN
7. FACING
8. FASHION
9. FINISH
10. FLANNEL
11. GABARDINE
12. GARMENT
13. HEM
14. HOOK AND EYE
15. KNIT
16. LINED
17. LINEN
18. MATERIAL
19. PATTERN
20. PLAID
21. PLEAT
22. SEAM
23. SILHOUETTE
24. SLIT
25. SUIT
26. TAILOR
27. TARTAN
28. VELOUR
29. WAISTBAND
30. WOOL
31. WRAP
32. WRINKLE
33. ZIPPER

```
X H T I U S E L E R A P P A
R B I A S J E L P N T J A A
X U E Y E D N A K O O H R H
N E O L S H T L M N R S W O
B T T L T T E N J O I N B R
F W A T E L R M G I U R O E
I A X R E V O A W H L L W P
N I N N T U B O D S I E T P
I S G A P A O F P A N N I I
S T U L R L N H T F E N L Z
H B E D I A L P L M N A S R
O A I N M A T E R I A L A K
T N E T I N K A A G S F E N
E D D E S I G N I C A F L E
```

1. BAKING SODA
2. BARLEY
3. CAKES
4. CANDLES
5. CANDY
6. CARDS
7. CEREAL
8. CHIPS
9. COOKIES
10. CRAYONS
11. DETERGENT
12. ENVELOPES
13. FROZEN FOODS
14. GAMES
15. GELATIN
16. MACARONI
17. MATCHES
18. NAILS
19. NOODLES
20. OATMEAL
21. PAPER
22. PENCILS
23. PIES
24. PRESENT
25. PUDDING MIX
26. RICE
27. SALT
28. TISSUES

```
Q O V O N A R A L S F G K I
P X N A E D E T E R G E N T
R I I T Z O H I O C I O K I
E L T M E S P Z O N R K D S
S J A E G G E O C A N D Y S
E B L A T N K L C E S M D U
N M E L F I I A D L R R R E
T O G O E K M D I N A E C S
J M O S C A D C D C A H A T
E D A D S B N Q E U O C K L
S E P O L E V N E Z P O E A
R E P A P E M A T C H E S S
C R A Y O N S A S P I H C G
Y E L R A B B B R G J L R X A
```

1. ANISE

2. BLACK

3. BOILING

4. CANDIES

5. CHERRY

6. COUGH DROPS

7. DRIED

8. EXTRACT

9. FLAVORFUL

10. GRAPE

11. GUMDROPS

12. HERB

13. JELLYBEANS

14. LACES

15. MEDICINE

16. MOVIE THEATER

17. ROPES

18. STICKS

19. STRAWBERRY

20. STRINGS

21. SWEET

22. TASTY

23. TWIZZLERS

24. WHIPS

```
G G S E I D N A C E M J Q F
D R L H E Y L F O X Z H Y E
M R A S S A G G U T Z Y T O
H O I P C L U Z G R Z O S E
Y N V E E M U R H A Q J A S
A R S I D O H F D C Z F T G
X Y R R E B W A R T S I W N
A K O E R T G S O O C W I I
Q P C E H N H W P K V O Z R
S P H A I C P E S F U A Z T
E J E L L Y B E A N S J L S
N A I E M B E T N T Q I E F
E O F M E D I C I N E T R Y
B T P W H I P S E P O R S P
```

1. ALTA
2. ARCHES
3. BLUFF
4. DELTA
5. ESCALANTE
6. EUREKA
7. GOSHEN
8. HYRUM
9. KAMAS
10. KANAB
11. KANOSH
12. LARK
13. LEHI
14. LEVAN
15. LOGAN
16. MAGNA
17. MOAB
18. MONA
19. NEOLA
20. OGDEN
21. PARADISE
22. PRICE
23. PROVO
24. SALINA
25. SALT LAKE
26. TROPIC
27. UNION
28. UNITA
29. VERNAL
30. ZION

```
S T N N E A U L Y B G Q C X
E U D A C N B A H Y R U M W
H N F G I U C A V S N B O O
C I P O R T N E H S O G Q E
R T N L P G R D Z K I N S L
A A T L A N E D N M Z I A I
K L Z M A L O P B E D P L K
E Q S L T P E I R A O R T K
R M O A B F L H R O N L L Q
U O E K L W F A I Q V A A Q
E N R E S I P U T M Q O K M
M A V O E T N A L A C S E F
L A O D S A M A K B V T L J
N E W S V C M N E D G O X J
```

1. ARABESQUE

2. BALANCE

3. BALLERINA

4. BARRE

5. BATTERIE

6. BRISE

7. CABRIOLE

8. CAMBRE

9. COUPE

10. DANSEUR

11. ELEVATION

12. ENTRECHAT

13. EXTENSION

14. FOUETTE

15. GLISSADE

16. JETE

17. PAR TERRE

18. PAS DE DEUX

19. PIROUETTE

20. PLIE

21. POINTE

22. POSITIONS

23. PROMENADE

24. TOUR

```
P O L K T E L B B O C X E V
D P F K T B T F S A R R X U
B H A E D A N E M O R P K P
L R U S L L H B J A U E C O
C P I D D L R C B U U A P I
N O I S N E T X E Q B I B N
O S U U E R D B S R R T A T
I I Q P Z I F E I O T E T E
T T L T E N B O U O I N T C
A I L Z K A L E U X E U E N
V O M N R E T R A E X R R A
E N P A R T E R R E T S I L
L S R U E S N A D L X T E A
E I L P Y G L I S S A D E B
```

1. AGATE
2. BEACH
3. COLLECTION
4. DISCOVERY
5. DISPLAY
6. EXCAVATION
7. FOSSILS
8. GEMS
9. GRANITE
10. HIKE
11. HILLS
12. HOBBY
13. LUCK
14. MOUNTAIN
15. POLISHING
16. RESEARCH
17. SCOOP
18. SCREEN
19. SHAPES
20. SIFTING
21. SPECIMENS
22. STREAMS
23. TUMBLER
24. VARIETY
25. WASHING

```
L H C S P L Q V C E H V P O
K P I T H B E A C H S N X L
C P R L M A U R E T V K E Y
U O E C L C P I R R X X R O
L L L G H S N E M I C E P S
C I B L E C A T S A V H P S
Y S M W E M R Y V O I Y U N
F H U A S C S A C K A Z E X
B I T S M L T S E L I E N H
Q N I H G I I I P S R B P U
B G Y I O D P S O C E M O A
M O U N T A I N S N C R O D
E T A G A D Y B B O H V C H
E T I N A R G N I T F I S Q
```

1. ANGLE

2. BALANCE

3. CHROME

4. CLUBS

5. FACE

6. GRIP

7. GROOVES

8. HEADS

9. IMPRINT

10. IRONS

11. LEATHER

12. LENGTH

13. MEASURE

14. METAL

15. PIECES

16. PLATE

17. PRECISE

18. RIDGES

19. SCREWS

20. SHAFT

21. SIZE

22. SLANT

23. SOLE

24. STEEL

25. STRAIGHT

26. STRONG

27. TEST

28. VARNISH

29. WEIGHT

30. WOOD

```
V V A R N I S H A F T S E T
Z R I H R A L E N G T H N K
U I A M N E C A V S B U L C
I D R G P N T E M O R H C A
O G L O A R C A S Z O T V T
H E E L N A I V L T S R H W
R S A D F S S N J P E G G K
S B T H G I A R T S I E S E
D M H R Z R R L I E G C L R
A V E E O H Q C W C R P A U
E D R T A N E U K E I D N S
H B F I A R G L W I P O T A
G X Q N P L C S O P S O L E
O I H L Q E M Z W H K W O M
```

1. ADMETUS
2. ADVENTURES
3. AESON
4. ARGO
5. BLACK SEA
6. CASTOR
7. COLCHIS
8. DANGERS
9. DRAGONS
10. ESCAPES
11. EXPLOITS
12. GOLDEN FLEECE
13. GREECE
14. HARPIES
15. HEROES
16. IOLCUS
17. ISLES
18. JASON
19. KINGDOM
20. LEGEND
21. LEMNOS
22. MEDEA
23. ORPHEUS
24. PELEUS
25. PURSUITS
26. QUEST
27. ROCKS
28. ROUTES
29. SHIPS
30. STORMS
31. TALOS
32. TASKS

```
N C A S T O R S O N M E L N
O I G T S V I S N T Q P L O
S S G I U H S G T O S E S S
E L R O C K S T R O G E W A
A E M L L Y U P I E R A U J
D S O P O D H A N U E M R Q
N C D X I E E D T H S C S D
H A G E U D W N A O N R E Z
H P N S E K E R F Q O O U M
E E I M H V P P E L E U S P
R S K Z D I S A D M E T U S
O G R A E S K C A L B E M E
E W L S R E G N A D J S C J
S H I P S K S A T A L O S E
```

1. AGED
2. AROMA
3. BEIGE
4. BLUE-GREEN
5. CLUMPING
6. CREAMY
7. DANISH
8. ENGLISH
9. FLAVOR
10. GORGONZOLA
11. GRATED
12. GRAYISH-BLUE
13. ITALIAN
14. IVORY-HUED
15. MOIST

16. PUNGENT
17. RICH
18. ROQUEFORT
19. SAGA BLUE
20. SALADS
21. SOFT
22. STILTON
23. STREAKED
24. STRONG
25. TEXTURE
26. UNITED STATES
27. VEINS
28. WEBBED
29. WHITE

```
S  E  E  T  I  H  W  X  Y  M  A  E  R  C
E  T  U  G  E  X  W  V  D  T  O  O  Q  S
T  N  R  L  I  R  T  E  H  P  V  I  D  S
A  E  E  E  B  E  U  L  B  A  G  A  S  C
T  G  M  U  A  H  B  T  L  B  L  C  L  T
S  N  T  J  Y  K  S  F  X  A  E  U  Y  B
D  U  R  R  S  M  E  I  S  E  M  D  L  H
E  P  O  I  T  T  A  D  Y  P  T  U  C  G
T  V  F  T  I  F  W  R  I  A  E  I  N  R
I  E  E  A  L  O  Z  N  O  G  R  O  G  A
N  I  U  L  T  S  G  R  R  M  R  G  T  T
U  N  Q  I  O  A  G  E  D  T  A  K  P  E
L  S  O  A  N  T  E  H  S  I  N  A  D  D
O  O  R  N  E  N  G  L  I  S  H  H  I  W
```

1. ALIEN

2. ANDROID

3. BRAINSTORM

4. DREAMSCAPE

5. EXCALIBUR

6. EXPLORERS

7. FREEJACK

8. FUTURE KICK

9. FUTUREWORLD

10. GREMLINS

11. HIGHLANDER

12. ICEMAN

13. INNERSPACE

14. LABYRINTH

15. LEGEND

16. PREDATOR

17. RODAN

18. SPACECAMP

19. SUPERGIRL

20. THEM

21. TRON

22. VIBES

23. WARGAMES

24. WESTWORLD

```
H D V N R P M A C E C A P S
U F I I C E M A N I C R C L
W U B O V Y D W N Y O N Z A
F T E B R A I N S T O R M B
W U S E H D E K A R R L V Y
N R T M X R N D T L D R R R
K E T U S P E A E L H I U I
C K I P R R L G R A V G B N
A I A L P E E O O N A R I T
J C G K A N W N R U Y E L H
E K O V D T Z O A E C P A E
E P A C S M A E R D R U C M
R G R E M L I N S L O S X A
F W W A R G A M E S D R E W
```

1. AIR CONDITIONER

2. ASPHALT

3. BALLOON

4. BASEBALL

5. BIRDS

6. CHIMNEY

7. FIBERGLASS

8. GARGOYLE

9. GUTTERS

10. KITE

11. LEAK

12. LEAVES

13. LIGHTNING ROD

14. MOSS

15. NAILS

16. NEWSPAPER

17. PATCH

18. RAIN

19. SEAMS

20. SHEET METAL

21. SHINGLES

22. SKYLIGHT

23. SLATE

24. SNOW

25. SQUIRREL

26. SUNLIGHT

27. TILE

28. VENT

29. WATERPROOFING

```
R  E  N  O  I  T  I  D  N  O  C  R  I  A
W  A  T  E  R  P  R  O  O  F  I  N  G  T
G  B  M  R  S  W  N  R  S  F  K  C  L  H
Y  A  B  M  S  O  O  G  L  I  I  A  C  G
Z  S  A  I  O  H  A  N  S  B  T  S  H  I
C  E  I  L  R  R  I  I  S  E  E  T  I  L
S  B  L  L  G  D  O  N  M  R  V  L  M  Y
P  A  X  O  E  P  S  T  G  G  T  A  N  K
B  L  Y  R  A  R  E  H  S  L  N  H  E  S
S  L  A  T  E  E  R  G  S  A  E  P  Y  L
E  I  C  T  H  N  A  I  L  S  V  S  T  G
N  H  T  S  K  A  E  L  U  S  O  A  I  A
S  U  N  L  I  G  H  T  E  Q  M  M  L  Q
G  G  T  G  T  R  E  P  A  P  S  W  E  N
```

1. ACCESSORY

2. BAG

3. BARRETTE

4. BASIC BLACK

5. BELT

6. BRACELET

7. CLASH

8. COLOR

9. COORDINATE

10. EARRINGS

11. FASHION

12. GLASSES

13. HAT

14. HOSE

15. MATCH

16. NAIL POLISH

17. NECKLACE

18. PURSE

19. SCARF

20. SHAWL

21. SHOES

22. SOCKS

23. STYLE

U	J	Y	S	E	S	S	A	L	G	K	E	N	M
H	K	N	I	T	E	S	O	H	A	S	E	W	K
R	J	O	M	A	T	C	H	C	R	C	F	W	E
R	L	I	J	N	D	P	T	U	K	B	B	Q	E
A	D	H	S	I	L	O	P	L	I	A	N	L	T
D	M	S	T	D	A	E	A	F	S	G	Y	S	T
F	T	A	U	R	Y	C	T	I	O	T	H	K	E
P	H	F	X	O	E	E	C	T	S	O	O	C	L
Q	T	C	T	O	U	B	H	E	E	B	A	O	E
L	T	L	L	C	L	G	N	S	S	R	S	S	C
V	W	A	E	A	R	R	I	N	G	S	R	C	A
V	J	A	C	B	S	C	Q	Y	L	E	O	A	R
X	W	K	H	S	K	H	I	C	O	L	O	R	B
H	G	J	U	S	D	M	R	A	J	M	Y	F	Y

1. ALUMINUM
2. CAP
3. CHANNEL
4. CLEAN
5. DEBRIS
6. DENT
7. DIVERSION
8. DOWNSPOUT
9. DRAIN
10. DURABLE
11. EAVES
12. ELBOW
13. EXTENSION
14. HOUSE
15. ICE
16. JOINER
17. LEAK
18. LIGHTWEIGHT
19. MITER
20. NAIL
21. OVERHANG
22. PEEL
23. PLASTIC
24. RUST
25. SCOOP
26. SEAL
27. SNOW
28. SPLASH
29. SPRING
30. STAINLESS STEEL
31. STRAINER
32. TEMPERATURE
33. VINYL
34. WATER

```
L E E T S S S E L N I A T S
C U P T U V R T S U R H E W
G H L P Q O K E L U G M M O
H S A L P S P A N I O K P B
R C S N A I L S E I C H E L
E N T D N M D W N L A L R E
N O I S N E T X E W B R A E
I I C I J H L A L A O L T P
O S A T G D N G R Y U D S
J R N I E L W U N M N P R E
D E L B C A D X I I T I E W
D V R X T E G N A H R E V O
M I T E R S U S C O O P I N
S D R O X M J F E A V E S S
```

1. BUTTER

2. CALORIES

3. CANDLE

4. CARBON

5. COCONUT

6. COD LIVER

7. COSMETICS

8. CREAM

9. DIET

10. DRUGS

11. DYES

12. FISH

13. FLAXSEED

14. FUEL

15. GLYCERIN

16. HALIBUT

17. HYDROGEN

18. LANOLIN

19. LARD

20. MARGARINE

21. PAINT

22. PALM OIL

23. PERFUME

24. SOAP

25. STEARIN

26. TUNG NUTS

27. WAX

```
S I R D S A M A E R C C T N
F E T C O C O N U T O H N W
G L Y C E R I N S D O W I C
E L A D D R O T L N W M A P
C M Z X A F E I E C N N P X
Z T U G S A V G I M D I A P
W C R F R E O W S L S L O K
U A J I R R E D E R T O S H
M L N Y D E R D R R U N C U
D O B Y Q A P E I U N A A T
A R H P L Y O V T F G L R U
L I O M L A P V U T N S B Q
T E I D P W X E V A U S O H
H S I F H A L I B U T B N H
```

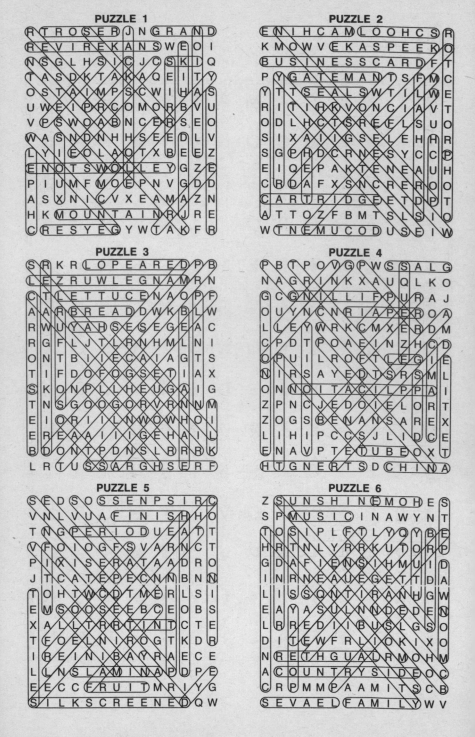

PUZZLE 1

PUZZLE 2

PUZZLE 3

PUZZLE 4

PUZZLE 5

PUZZLE 6

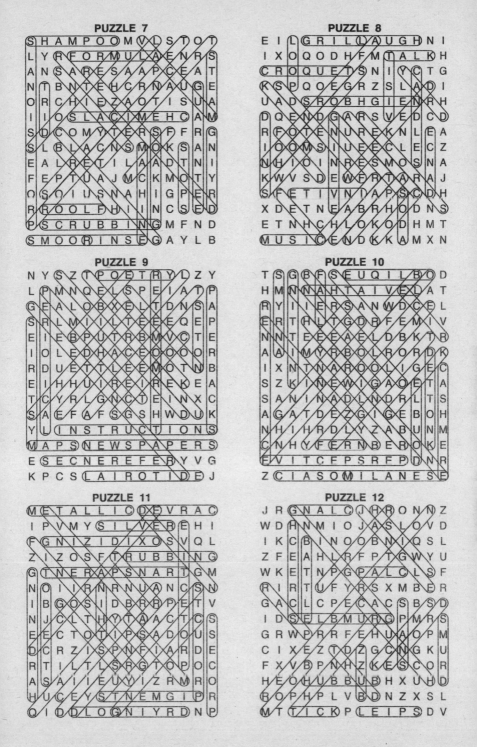

PUZZLE 7

```
S H A M P O O M V L S T O T
L Y R F O R M U L A E N R S
A N S A R E S A A P C E A T
N T B N T E H C R N A U G E
O R C H I E Z A O T I S U A
I I O S L A C I M E H C A M
S O C O M Y T E R S F F R G
S L B L A C N S M O K S A N
E A L R E T I L A A D T N I
F E P T U A J M C K M O T Y
O S O I U S N A H I G P E R
R R O O L F H I I N C S E D
P S C R U B B I N G M F N D
S M O O R I N S E G A Y L B
```

PUZZLE 8

```
E I L G R I L L A U G H N I
I X O Q O D H F M T A L K H
C R O Q U E T S N I Y C T G
K S P Q O E G R Z S L A D I
U A D S R O B H G I I E N R
D Q E N D G A R S V E D C D
R F O T E N U R E K N L E A
I O O M S I U E E C L E C Z
N H I O I N R E S M O S N A
K W V S D E W F R T A R A J
S F E T I V N A P S C D H
X D E T N E A B R H O D N S
E T N H C H L O K O D H M T
M U S I C E N D K K A M X N
```

PUZZLE 9

```
N Y S Z T P O E T R Y L Z Y
L P M N Q E L S P E I A T P
G E A L O B X E L T D N S A
S R L M I I L T E E E Q E P
E I E B P U T R B M V C T E
I O L E D H A C E O O O R
R D U E T T L E E M O T N B
E I H H U I R E I R E K E A
T C Y R L G N C T E I N X C
S A E F A F S G S H W D U K
Y U I N S T R U C T I O N S
M A P S N E W S P A P E R S
E S E C N E R E F E R Y V G
K P C S L A I R O T I D E J
```

PUZZLE 10

```
T S G B F S E U Q I L B O D
H M N N A H T A I V E L A T
R Y I I E R S A N W D C E L
E R T H L T G D B F E M I V
N N T E X E A E L D B K T B
A A I M Y R B O L R O R D K
I X N T N A R O O L I G E C
S Z K I N E W I G A O E T A
S A N I N A D L N D R L T S
A G A T D E Z G I G E B O H
N H I H R D L Y Z A B U N M
C N H Y F E R N B E R O K E
F V I T C F P S R F P D N R
Z C I A S O M I L A N E S E
```

PUZZLE 11

```
M E T A L L I C O X E V R A C
I P V M Y S I L V E R E H I
F G N I Z I D I X O S V Q L
Z I Z O S F T R U B B I N G
G T N E R A P S N A R T G M
N O I I R N R N U A N C S N
I B G O S I D B R R P E T V
N J C L T H Y T A A C T C S
E E C T O T I P S A D O U S
D C R Z I S P N F I A R D E
R T I L T L S R G T O P O C
A S A I I E U Y I Z R M R O
H U C E Y S T N E M G I P R
Q I D D L O G N I Y R D N P
```

PUZZLE 12

```
J R G N A L O J H R O N N Z
W D H N M I O J A S L O V D
I K C B I N O O B N I Q S L
Z F E A H L R F P T G W Y U
W K E T N P G P A L C L S F
R I R T U F Y R S X M B E R
G A C L C P E C A C S B S D
I D S E L B M U R C P M R S
G R W P R R F E H U A O P M
C I X E Z T D Z G C N G K U
F X V B P N H Z K E S C O R
H E O H U B B U B H X U H D
R O P H P L V B D N Z X S L
M T T I C K P L E I P S D V
```

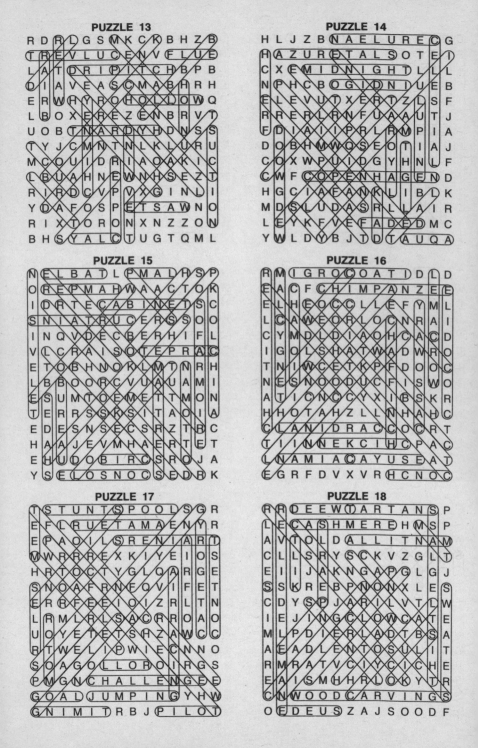

PUZZLE 13

PUZZLE 14

PUZZLE 15

PUZZLE 16

PUZZLE 17

PUZZLE 18

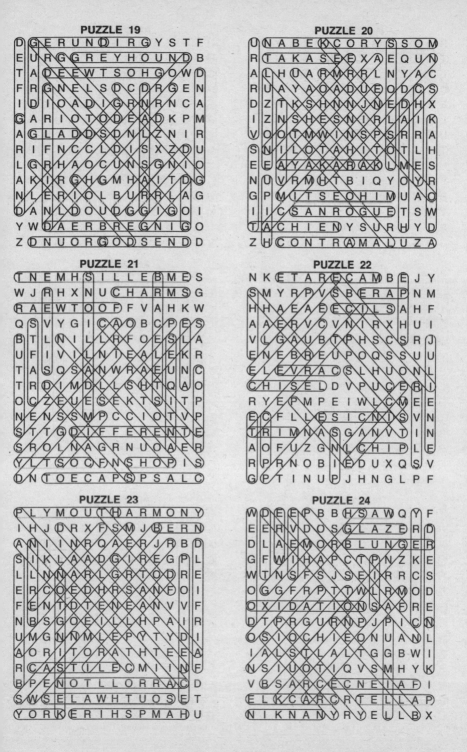

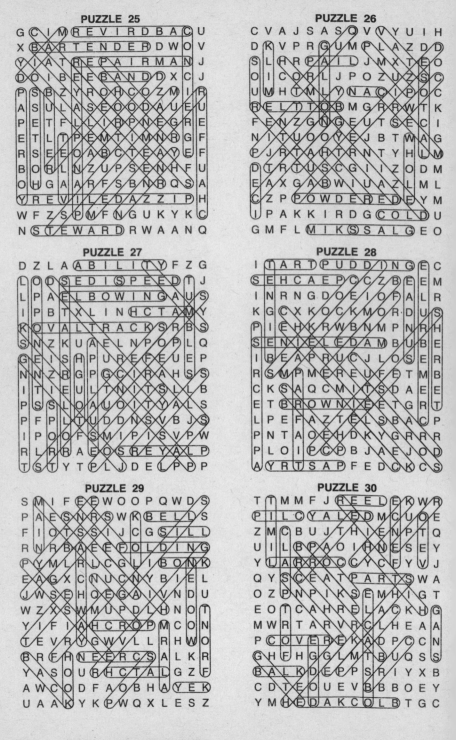

PUZZLE 25

```
G C I M R E V I R D B A C U
X B A R T E N D E R D W O V
Y I A T R E P A I R M A N J
D O I B E E B A N D D X C J
P S B Z Y R O H C O Z M I R
A S U L A S E O O D A U E U
P E T F L L I R P N E G R E
E T L T P E M T I M N B G F
R S E E O A B C T E A Y E F
B O R L N Z U P S E N H F U
O H G A A R F S B N R Q S A
Y R E V I L E D A Z Z I P H
W F Z S P M F N G U K Y K C
N S T E W A R D R W A A N Q
```

PUZZLE 26

```
C V A J S A S O V V Y U I H
D K V P R G U M P L A Z D D
S L H R P A I L J M X T E O
O I C O R L J P O Z U Z S C
U M H T M L Y N A C I P O C
R E L T T O B M G R R W T K
F E N Z G N G E U T S E C I
N I T U O O V E J B T W A G
P J R T A H T R N T Y H L M
D R T U S C G I I Z O D M
E A X G A B W I U A Z L M L
C Z P P O W D E R E D E Y M
I P A K K I R D G C O L D U
G M F L M I K S S A L G E O
```

PUZZLE 27

```
D Z L A A B I L I T Y F Z G
L O O S E D I S P E E D T J
I P A E L B O W I N G A U S
I P B T X L I N H C T A M Y
K O V A L T R A C K S R B S
S N Z K U A E L N P O P L Q
G E I S H P U R E F E U E P
N N Z R B G P G C R H A S S
I T I E U L T N I T S L L B
P S S L O A U O I T Y A L S
P F P L T U D D N S V B J S
I P O O F S M I P I S V P W
R L R B A E O S R E Y X L P
T S T Y T P L J D E L P P P
```

PUZZLE 28

```
I T A R T P U D D I N G E C
S E H C A E P C C Z B E E M
I N R N G D O E I O F A L R
K G C X K O C K M O R D U S
P I E H K R W B N M P N R H
S E N X E L E D A M B U B E
I B E A P R U C J L O S E R
R S M P M E R E U F E T M B
C K S A Q C M T S D A E E
E T B R O W N X E E T G R T
L P E F A Z T E L S B A C P
P N T A O E H D K Y G R R R
P L O I P C P B J A E J O D
A Y R T S A P F E D C K C S
```

PUZZLE 29

```
S M I F E E W O O P Q W D S
P A E S N R S W K B E L L S
F I O T S S I J C G S I L L
R N R B A E E O L D I N G
P Y M L R L C G L I B O N K
E A G X C N U C N Y B I E L
J W S E H O E G A I V N D U
W Z X S W M U P D L H N O T
Y I F I X A H C R O P M C O N
T E V R Y G W V L L R H W O
B R F H N E X E R C S A L K R
Y A S O U R H C T A L G Z F
A W C O D F A O B H A Y E K
U A A K Y K P W Q X L E S Z
```

PUZZLE 30

```
T T M M F J R E E L E K W R
P I L C Y A L E D M C U O E
Z M C B U J T H I E N P T Q
U I L B P A O I H N E S E Y
Y L A R R O C C Y C F Y V J
Q Y S C E A T P A R T S W A
O Z P N P I K S E M H I G T
E O T C A H R E L A C K H G
M W R T A R V R C L H E A A
P C O V E R E K A D P C C N
G H F H G G L M T B U Q S S
B A L K D E P P S R I Y X B
C D T E O U E V B B B O E Y
Y M H E D A K C O L B T G C
```

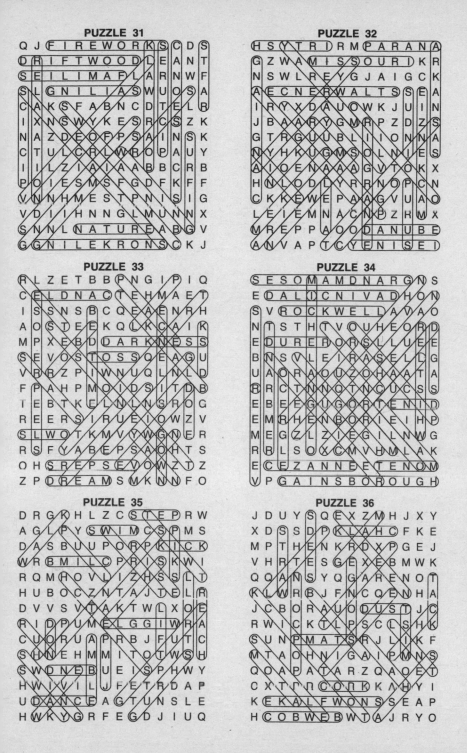

PUZZLE 31

```
Q J F I R E W O R K S C D S
D R I F T W O O D L E A N T
S E I L I M A P L A R N W F
S L G N I L I A S W U O S A
C A K S F A B N C D T E L R
I X N S W Y K E S R C S Z K
N A Z D E O P S A I N S K
C T U L C R L W R O P A U Y
I I L Z I X I A A B B C R B
P O I E S M S F G D F K F F
V N N H M E S T P N I S I G
V D I I H N N G L M U N N X
S N N L N A T U R E A B G V
G G N I L E K R O N S C K J
```

PUZZLE 32

```
H S Y T R I R M P A R A N A
G Z W A M I S S O U R I K R
N S W L R E Y G J A I G C K
A E C N E R W A L T S S E A
I R Y X D A U O W K J U I N
J B A A R V G M R P Z D Z S
G T R G U U B L I I O N N A
N Y H K U G M S O L N I E S
A I O E N A A A G V T O K X
H N L O D L Y R R N O P C N
C K K E W E P A X G V U A O
L E I E M N A C N P Z H W X
M R E P P A O O D A N U B E
A N V A P T C Y E N I S E I
```

PUZZLE 33

```
R L Z E T B B P N G I P I Q
C E L D N A C T E H M A E T
I S S N S B C Q E X E N R H
A O S T E E K Q L K C A I K
M P X E B D D A R K N E S S
S E V O S T O S S Q E A G U
V R R Z P I W N U Q L N L D
F P A H P M O I D S I T D B
T E B T K E L N L N G R O G
R E E R S I R U E I O W Z V
S L W O T K M V Y W G N E R
R S F Y A B E P S A O H T S
O H S R E P S E V O W Z T Z
Z P D R E A M S M K N N F O
```

PUZZLE 34

```
S E S O M A M D N A R G N S
E D A L I C N I V A D H O N
S V R O C K W E L L A V A O
N T S T H T V O U H E O R D
E D U R E R O R S L L U E E
B N S V L E I R A S E L L G
U A O R A O U Z O H A X A T A
R R C T N N Q T N C U C S S
E B E E G U G O R T E N I D
E M R H E N B O R I E I H P
M E G Z L Z I E G I L N W G
R B L S O X C M V H M L A K
E C E Z A N N E E T E N O M
V P G A I N S B O R O U G H
```

PUZZLE 35

```
D R G K H L Z C S T E P R W
A G L P Y S W I M C S P M S
D A S B U U P O R P K I C K
W R B M L C P R I S K W I
R Q M H O V L I Z H S S L T
H U B O C Z N T A J T E L R
D V V S V T A K T W L X O E
R I D P U M E L G G I I W R A
C U O R U A P R B J F U T C
S I N E H M M I T O T W S H
S W O N E B U E I S P H W Y
H W I V I L J F E T R D A P
U D X N C E A G T U N S L E
H W K Y G R F E G D J I U Q
```

PUZZLE 36

```
J D U Y S Q E X Z M H J X Y
X D S S D P K L X A H C F K E
M P T H E N K R D X P G E J
V H R T E S G E X E B M W K
Q Q A N S Y Q G A R E N O T
K L W R B J F N C Q E N H A
J C B O R A U O U S T J C
R W I C K T L P S C L S H K
S U N P M A T S R J L I K F
M T A O H N I G A I P M N S
Q O A P A T A R Z Q A O E T
C X T T C O N K A H Y I
K E K A L F W O N S S E A P
H C O B W E B W T A J R Y O
```

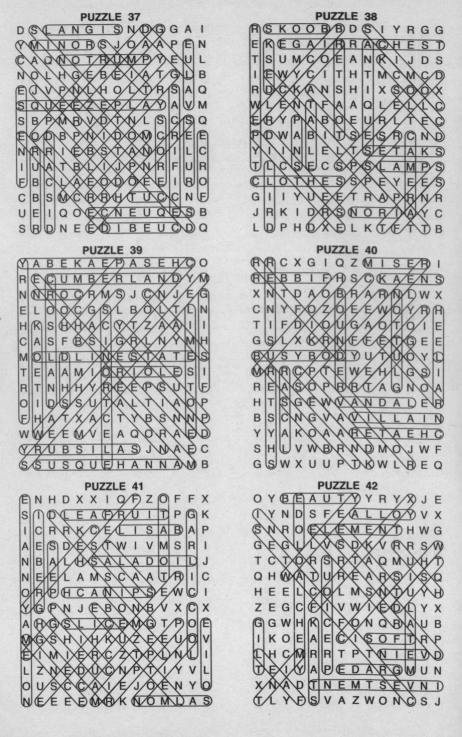

PUZZLE 37

```
D S L A N G I S N G G A I
Y M I N O R S J O A A P E N
C A Q N O T R U M P Y E U L
N O L H G E B E I A T G L B
E J V P N L H O L T R S A Q
S Q U X E X Z P L A Y A V M
S B P M R V D T N L S C S Q
E O D B P N I D O M C R E E
N R R I E B S T A N O I L C
I U A T B L I J P N R F U R
F B C L A E O D O E E I R O
C B S M C R R H T U C C N F
U E I Q O E C N E U Q E S B
S R D N E E D I B E U C D Q
```

PUZZLE 38

```
R S K O O B B D S I Y R G G
E K E G A I R R A C H E S T
T S U M C O E A N K I J D S
I E W Y C I T H T M C M C D
R D C K A N S H I X S O O X
W L E N T F A A Q L E L L C
E R Y P A B O E U R L T E C
P D W A B I T S E S R C N D
Y I I N L E L T S E T A K S
T L C S E C S P S L A M P S
C L O T H E S S P E Y E E S
G I I Y U E X T R A P R N R
J R K I D R S N O R I A Y C
L D P H O X E L K T F T T B
```

PUZZLE 39

```
Y A B E K A E P A S E H C O
R E C U M B E R L A N D Y M
N N R O C R M S J C N J E G
E L O O C G S L B O L T L N
H K S H H A C Y T Z A A I I
C A S F B S I G R L N Y M H
M O L D L I X E S T A T E S
T E A A M I O R I O L E S I
R T N H H Y R E E P S U T F
O I D S S U T A L T I A O P
F H A T X A C T Y B S N N P
W W E E M V E A Q O R A E D
Y R U B S I L A S J N A E C
S S U S Q U E H A N N A M B
```

PUZZLE 40

```
R R C X G I Q Z M I S E R I
R E B B I F H S C K A E N S
X N T D A O B R A R N D W X
C N Y F O Z O E E W O Y R H
T I F D I O U G A O T O I E
G S L X K R N F E E T G E E
B U S Y B O D Y U T U O Y L
M R R C P T E W E H L G S I
R E A S O P R R T A G N O A
H T S G E W V A N D A L E R
B S C N G V A V I L L A I N
Y Y A K O A A R E T A E H C
S H L V W B R N D M O J W F
G S W X U U P T K W L R E Q
```

PUZZLE 41

```
E N H D X X I O F Z O F F X
S I O L E A F R U I T P G K
I C R R K C E L I S A B A P
A E S D E S T W I V M S R I
N B A L H S A L A D O I L J
N E E L A M S C A A T R I C
O R P H C A N I P S E W C I
Y G P N J E B O N B V X C X
A H G S L I C E M G T P O E
M G S H I H K U Z E E U O V
E I M I E R C Z T P L N L I
L Z N E D U C N P T I Y V L
O U S C C A I E J O E N Y O
N E E E E M R K N O M L A S
```

PUZZLE 42

```
O Y B E A U T Y Y R Y X J E
I Y N D S F E A L L O Y V X
S N R O E L E M E N T H W G
G E G L L V S D K V R R S W
T C T O R S R T A Q M U H T
Q H W A T U R E A R S I S Q
H E E L C O L M S N T U Y H
Z E G C E I V W I E D L Y X
G G W H K C F O N Q B A U B
I K O E A E C I S O F T R P
L H C M R R T P T N I E V D
T E X I Y A P E D A R G M U N
X N A D T N E M T S E V N I
T L Y F S V A Z W O N C S J
```

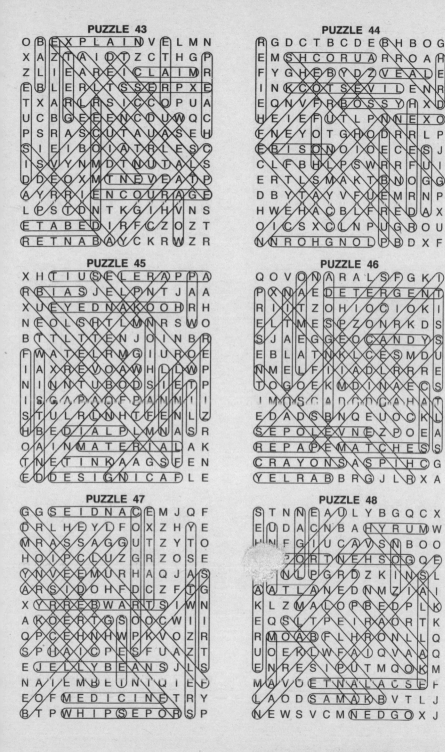

PUZZLE 43

```
O B E X P L A I N V E L M N
X A Z T A I D T Z C T H G P
Z L I E A R E I C L A I M R
E B L E R L T S S E R P X E
T X A R L R S I C C O P U A
U C B G E E E N C D U W Q C
P S R A S C U T A U A S E H
S I E I B O I A T R L E S C
I S V Y N M D T N U T A L S
D D E O X M T N E V E A T P
A Y R R I E N C O U R A G E
L P S T D N T K G I H V N S
E T A B E D I R F C Z O Z T
R E T N A B A Y C K R W Z R
```

PUZZLE 44

```
R G D C T B C D E B H B O G
E M S H C O R U A R R O A H
F Y G H E B Y D Z V E A L E
I N K C O T S E V I L E N R
E Q N V F R B O S S Y H X D
H E I E F U T L P N N E X O
C N E Y O T G H O D R R L P
E B I S O N O I O E C E S J
C L F B H L P S W R R F U I
E R T L S M A K T B N O G G
D B Y T A Y V F U E M R N P
H W E H A C B L F R E D A X
O I C S X C L N P U G R O U
N N R O H G N O L P B D X F
```

PUZZLE 45

```
X H T I U S E L E R A P P A
R B I A S J E L P N T J A A
X U E Y E D N A X O O H R H
N E O L S H T L M N R S W O
B T T L T T E N J O I N B R
F W A T E L R M G I U R O E
I A X R E V O A W H L L W P
N I N T U B O D S I E T P
I S G A P A O F B A N N I I
S T U L R O N H T F E N L Z
H B E D I A L P L M N A S R
O A I N M A T E R I A L A K
T N E T I N K A A G S F E N
E D D E S I G N I C A P L E
```

PUZZLE 46

```
Q O V O N A R A L S F G K I
P X N A E D E T E R G E N T
R I X T Z O H I O C I O K I
E L T M E S P Z O N R K D S
S J A E G G E O C A N D Y S
E B L A T N K L C E S M D U
N M E L F I K I A D L R R E
T O G O E K M D I N A E C S
I M O S C A D D C A H A T
E D A D S B N Q E U O C K L
S E P O L E V N E Z P O E A
R E P A P E M A T C H E S
C R A Y O N S A S P I H C G
Y E L R A B B R G J L R X A
```

PUZZLE 47

```
G G S E I D N A C E M J Q F
O R L H E Y L F O X Z H Y E
M R A S S A G G U T Z Y T O
H O I P C L U Z G R Z O S E
Y N V E E M U R H A Q J A S
A R S I D O H F D C Z F T G
X Y R R E B W A R T S I W N
A K O E R T G S O O C W I I
Q P C E H H N H W P K V O Z R
S P I A S I C P E S F U A Z T
E J E L L Y B E A N S J L S
N A I E M B E U N I Q I E F
E O F M E D I C I N E T R Y
B T P W H I P S E P O R S P
```

PUZZLE 48

```
S T N N E A U L Y B G Q C X
E U D A C N B A H Y R U M W
H N F G I U C A V S N B O O
R P O R T N E H S O G O E
N U P G R D Z K I N S L
A A T L A N E D N M Z I A I
K L Z M A L O P B E D P L K
E Q S L T P E I R A O R T K
R M O A B F L H R O N L L O
U O E K L W F A I Q V A A Q
E N R E S I P U T M Q O K M
M A V O E T N A L A C S F
L A O D S A M A K B V T L J
N E W S V C M N E D G O X J
```

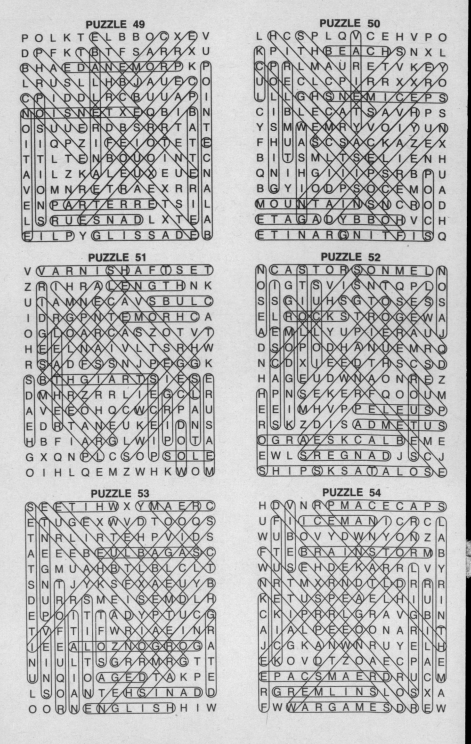

PUZZLE 49

```
P O L K T E L B B O C X E V
D P F K T B T F S A R R X U
B H A E D A N E M O R P K P
L R U S L L H B J A U E C O
C P I D D L R C B U U A P I
N O I S N E T X E O B I B N
O S U U E R D B S R R T A T
I I Q P Z I F E I O T E T E
T T L T E N B O U O I N T C
A I L Z K A L E U X E U E N
V O M N R E T R A E X R R A
E N P A R T E R R E T S I L
L S R U E S N A D L X T E A
E I L P Y G L I S S A D E B
```

PUZZLE 50

```
L A C S P L Q V C E H V P O
K P I T H B E A C H S N X L
C P R L M A U R E T V K E Y
U O E C L C P I R R X X R O
L L L G H S N E M I C E P S
C I B L E C A T S A V H P S
Y S M M E M R Y V O I Y U N
F H U A S C S A C K A Z E X
B I T S M L T S E L I E N H
Q N I H G I I I P S R B P U
B G Y I O D P S O C E M O A
M O U N T A I N S N C R O D
E T A G A D Y B B O H V C H
E T I N A R G N I T F I S Q
```

PUZZLE 51

```
V A R N I S H A F T S E T
Z R I H R A L E N G T H N K
U I A M N E C A V S B U L C
I D R G P N T E M O R H C A
O G L O A R C A S Z O T V T
H E E L N A I V L T S R H W
R S A D F S S N J P E G G K
S B T H G I A R T S I E S E
D A M H R Z R R L I E G C L R
A V E E O H Q C W C R P A U
E D R T A N E U K E I D N S
H B F I A R G L W I P O T A
G X Q N P L C S O P S O L E
O I H L Q E M Z W H K W O M
```

PUZZLE 52

```
N C A S T O R S O N M E L N
O I G T S V I S N T Q P L O
S S G I U H S G T O S E S S
E L R O C K S T R O G E W A
A E M L L Y U P X E R A U J
D S O P O D H A N U E M R Q
N C D X I E E D T H S C S D
H A G E U D W N A O N R E Z
H P N S E K E R F Q O O U M
E E I M H V P P E L E U S P
R S K Z D I S A D M E T U S
O G R A E S K C A L B E M E
E W L S R E G N A D J S C J
S H I P S K S A T A L O S E
```

PUZZLE 53

```
S E E T I H W X Y M A E R C
E T U G E X W V D T O O Q S
T N R L I R T E H P V I D S
A E E E B E U L B A G A S C
G M U A H B T L B L C L T
S N T J Y K S F X A E U Y B
D U R R S M E I S E M D L H
E P O I T T A D Y P T U C G
T V F T I F W R I A E I N R
I E E A L O Z N O G R O G A
N I U L T S G R R M R G T T
U N Q I O A G E D T A K P E
L S O A N T E H S I N A D D
O O R N E N G L I S H H I W
```

PUZZLE 54

```
H D V N R P M A C E C A P S
U F I I C E M A N I C R C L
W U B O V Y D W N Y O N Z A
F T E B R A I N S T O R M B
W U S E H D E K A R R L V Y
N R T M X R N D T L D R R R
K E T U S P E A E L H I U I
C K I P R R L G R A V G B N
A I A L P E E O O N A R I T
J C G K A N W N R U Y E L H
E K O V O T Z O A E C P A E
E P A C S M A E R D R U C M
R G R E M L I N S L O S X A
F W W A R G A M E S D R E W
```

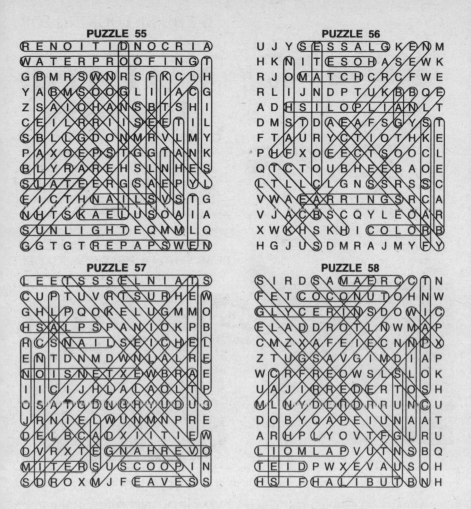

PUZZLE 55

```
R E N O I T I D N O C R I A
W A T E R P R O O F I N G T
G B M R S W N R S F K C D H
Y A B M S O O G L I I A C G
Z S A I O H A N S B T S H I
C E I L R R I I S E E I I L
S B L L G D O N M R V L M Y
P A X O E P S T G G T A N K
B L Y R A R E H S L N H E S
S L A T E E R G S A E P Y L
E I C T H N A I L S V S T G
N H T S K A E L U S O A I A
S U N L I G H T E Q M M L Q
G G T G T R E P A P S W E N
```

PUZZLE 56

```
U J Y S E S S A L G K E N M
H K N I T E S O H A S E W K
R J O M A T C H C R C F W E
R L I J N D P T U K B B Q E
A D H S I L O P L I A N L T
D M S T D A E A F S G Y S T
F T A U R Y C T I O T H K E
P H F X O E C T S O O C L L
Q T C T O U B H E E B A O E
L T L L C L G N S S R S S C
V W A E A R R I N G S R C A
V J A C B S C Q Y L E O A R
X W K H S K H I C O L O R B
H G J U S D M R A J M Y F Y
```

PUZZLE 57

```
L E E T S S S E L N I A T S
C U P T U V R T S U R H E W
G H L P Q O K E L U G M M O
H S A L P S P A N I O K P B
R C S N A I L S E I C H E L
E N T D N M D W N L A L R E
N O I S N E T X E W B R A E
I I C I J H L A L A O L T P
O S A T G D N G R Y U D U J
J R N I E L W U N M N P R E
O E L B C A D X I I T I E W
O V R X T E G N A H R E V O
M I T E R S U S C O O P I N
S O R O X M J F E A V E S S
```

PUZZLE 58

```
S I R D S A M A E R C C T N
F E T C O C O N U T O H N W
G L Y C E R I N S D O W I C
E L A D D R O T L N W M A P
C M Z X A F E I E C N N D X
Z T U G S A V G I M D I A P
W C R F R E O W S L S L O K
U A J I R R E D E R T O S H
M L N Y D D T D R U N C U
D O B Y Q A P E I U N A A T
A R H P L Y O V T F G L R U
L I O M L A P V U T N S B Q
T E I D P W X E V A U S O H
H S I F H A L I B U T B N H
```

7835.b/12-08/bw